Our
Old Fashioned
Country Diary
— for —
1985

edited by
Linda Campbell Franklin
designed by Sonja Douglas

Tree Communications, Inc.
New York

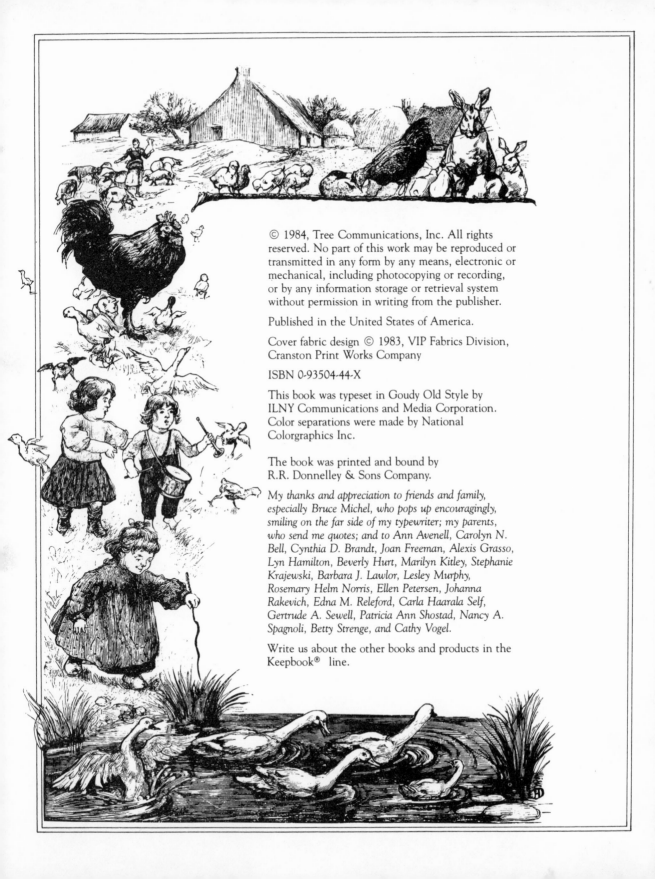

Published in the United States of America.

Cover fabric design © 1983, VIP Fabrics Division, Cranston Print Works Company

ISBN 0-93504-44-X

This book was typeset in Goudy Old Style by ILNY Communications and Media Corporation. Color separations were made by National Colorgraphics Inc.

The book was printed and bound by R.R. Donnelley & Sons Company.

My thanks and appreciation to friends and family, especially Bruce Michel, who pops up encouragingly, smiling on the far side of my typewriter; my parents, who send me quotes; and to Ann Avenell, Carolyn N. Bell, Cynthia D. Brandt, Joan Freeman, Alexis Grasso, Lyn Hamilton, Beverly Hurt, Marilyn Kitley, Stephanie Krajewski, Barbara J. Lawlor, Lesley Murphy, Rosemary Helm Norris, Ellen Petersen, Johanna Rakevich, Edna M. Releford, Carla Haarala Self, Gertrude A. Sewell, Patricia Ann Shostad, Nancy A. Spagnoli, Betty Strenge, and Cathy Vogel.

Write us about the other books and products in the Keepbook® line.

Dear Friends,

Thought has been on my mind a lot lately, as I collected for the sixth version of the diary. Conscious, willful thought about subjects of great concern. I'm afraid of the computer age, not because of mechanical mysteries, but because it encourages people, more and more, to depend on computers to be their memory, their senses, their intuition, even their teachers. Where has thinking gone, when we need the benefits of it more than ever?

For those of you who have been with us for several years, it will come as no surprise that in such a "pretty" book there are serious ideas, expressed by writers in the past and still worth considering.

In the old-fashioned spirit of this diary, I ask you to spend a little bit of time every day in 1985 trying to think! In the words of John Locke (*An Essay on Human Understanding*, 1690), it's in your power, when you turn your "eyes sometimes towards an object" to choose whether you "will curiously survey it, and with an intent application endeavour to observe accurately all that is visible in it."

May your 1985 be filled with splendid discoveries and many opportunities!

Sincerely,

Linda Campbell Franklin

Our Portrait Gallery

Jump, grin, smile pout;
Up, down, inside, out;
Serious, happy, sad, silly;
Year's start, year's end, willy-nilly.

*L*ooking *A*head in 1985

Tho' some things are planned, don't be surprised,
If nineteen-eighty-five isn't comprised
Of some of the following deeds and events,
Even if now they don't make sense!

New Year Greeting

Today's weather:

New Year's

How we celebrated New Year's Eve

Hopes and Resolutions

We spent
New Year's Day
this way

Menu
or
Special Recipe

A Memento of the Day

Write a Friend

"It was very pleasant to me to get a letter from you the other day. Perhaps I should have found it pleasanter if I had been able to decipher it. I don't think that I mastered anything beyond the date (which I knew) and the signature (which I guessed at). There's a singular and perpetual charm in a letter of yours; it never grows old, it never loses its novelty. . . . Other letters are read and thrown away. . .but yours are kept forever—unread. One of them will last a reasonable man a lifetime."

From letter to Edward S. Morse, from
Thomas Bailey Aldrich

January brings the snow,
Makes our feet and fingers glow.
Sarah Coleridge

"God has made the intellectual world harmonious and beautiful without us; but it will never come into our heads all at once; we must bring it home piece-meal, and there set it up by our own industry, or else we shall have nothing but darkness and a chaos within, whatever order and light there be in things without us."

John Locke, An Essay Concerning Human Understanding, 1690

Appointments
31 Monday *Soldier/statesman George Catlett Marshall born, 1880*
1 Tuesday *New Year's Day* *Rose, Orange & Sugar Bowls played: Touchdown!*
2 Wednesday *Gen. Washington's 13-stripe Continental Army flag flown, 1776*
3 Thursday *Author of Leaf, by Niggle, J.R.R. Tolkein, born, 1892*
4 Friday *Touch-reading-system inventor Louis Braille born, 1809*
5 Saturday *Billie Holiday recorded "When You're Smiling," 1938*
6 Sunday *Twelfth Day—Feast of the Epiphany*

December January

Diary

	1985					
	January					
Sun	Mon	Tue	Wed	Thu	Fri	Sat
		1	2	3	4	5
6	7	8	9	10	11	12
13	14	15	16	17	18	19
20	21	22	23	24	25	26
27	28	29	30	31		

"You must welcome all change with joy. And there is one other thing that is very important. You must breathe properly and let God take you by the hand."

Jacques-Henri Lartigue, French photographer, in 1982 interview

Appointments
7 Monday
Eerie cartoonist Charles Addams born, 1912
8 Tuesday
Russian Christmas celebrated   *Old Hickory's Day—last battle in War of 1812*
9 Wednesday
1st successful US manned-balloon ascension, Philadelphia, 1793
10 Thursday
League of Nations founded, 1920   *UN General Assembly met first time, 1946*
11 Friday
Statesman Alexander Hamilton born, in West Indies, 1757
12 Saturday
America's 1st public museum, in Charleston SC, opened, 1773
13 Sunday
Champion of upward struggle, Horatio Alger, born, 1834

January

Diary

1985
January

Sun	Mon	Tue	Wed	Thu	Fri	Sat
		1	2	3	4	5
6	7	8	9	10	11	12
13	14	15	16	17	18	19
20	21	22	23	24	25	26
27	28	29	30	31		

Appointments

14 Monday

Author John Dos Passos born, 1896

15 Tuesday

Leader & visionary Martin Luther King, Jr., born, 1929

16 Wednesday

Great performer Ethel Merman born, 1909

17 Thursday

St. Anthony's Day—Blessing of the Animals
Elder Statesman Benjamin Franklin born, 1706

18 Friday

Captain Cook discovered Hawaii, 1778

19 Saturday

Steam engine inventor James Watt born, 1736

20 Sunday

World Religion Day
1st basketball game played, Springfield MA, 1892

"If we feared the entertaining of an unverifiable opinion with the warmth with which we fear using the wrong implement at the dinner table, if the thought of holding a prejudice disgusted us as does a foul disease, then the dangers of man's suggestibility would be turned into advantages."

William Trotter, Instincts of the Herd

January

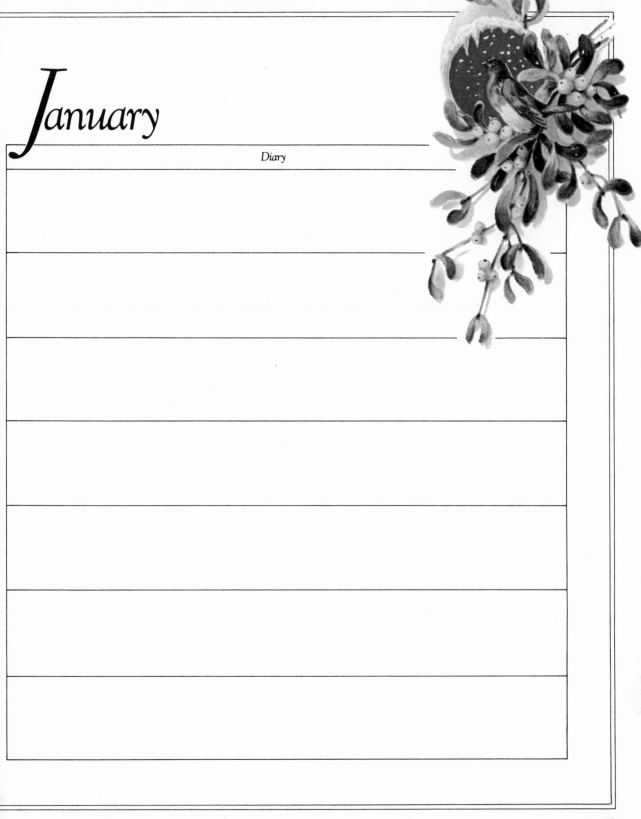

Diary

1985
January

Sun	Mon	Tue	Wed	Thu	Fri	Sat
		1	2	3	4	5
6	7	8	9	10	11	12
13	14	15	16	17	18	19
20	21	22	23	24	25	26
27	28	29	30	31		

How to Eat Candy
I had a box of candy, once;
   I put it on the shelf,
And every now and then I went
   and had a bite myself.

It tasted good, but, afterwhile,
   Although it was my own,
I felt just like a greedy pig,
   To eat it all alone.

And so I passed it all around,
   From Father down to "Dandy,"
And, really, *that's* the nicest way
   To eat a box of candy!

Charles Irvin Junkin, in "Little Folks," January 1915

Appointments

21 Monday

Clockmaker & inventor John Fitch born, 1743

22 Tuesday

English poet George Byron born, 1788

23 Wednesday

National Handwriting Day
Actor Humphrey Bogart born, 1899

24 Thursday

Ballerina Maria Tallchief born, 1925

25 Friday

Scottish poet Robert Burns born, 1759

26 Saturday

1st successful hydroplane, "Flying Fish," piloted, 1911

27 Sunday

1st public demonstration of TV, in Scotland, 1926

January

Diary

February

Sun	Mon	Tue	Wed	Thu	Fri	Sat
					1	2
3	4	5	6	7	8	9
10	11	12	13	14	15	16
17	18	19	20	21	22	23
24	25	26	27	28		

Hate and mistrust are the children of blindness,—/Could we but see one another, 'twere well!/ Knowledge is sympathy, charity, kindness,/ Ignorance only is maker of hell./ Could we but gaze for an hour, for a minute,/ Deep in each other's unfaltering eyes,/ Love were begun—for that look would begin it—/Born in the flash of a mighty surprise.

Sir William Watson, from "England to Ireland"

February brings the rain,
Thaws the frozen earth again.
Sarah Coleridge

Appointments
28 Monday
Word "serendipity" coined by Horace Walpole, 1754
29 Tuesday
Comedian W.C. Fields (Claude William Dukenfield) born, 1880
30 Wednesday
Actress Carol Channing born, 1923
31 Thursday
Ballerina Anna Pavlova born, 1885
1 Friday
National Freedom Day *Black History Month begins*
2 Saturday
Candlemas Day & Groundhog Day
3 Sunday
1st woman M.D. in America, Elizabeth Blackwell, born, 1821

January *February*

Diary

February

February

Sun	Mon	Tue	Wed	Thu	Fri	Sat
					1	2
3	4	5	6	7	8	9
10	11	12	13	14	15	16
17	18	19	20	21	22	23
24	25	26	27	28		

"God sends children...to enlarge our hearts, to make us unselfish, and full of kindly sympathies and affections...and to call out all our faculties to extended enterprise and exertion; to bring round our fireside bright faces and happy smiles, and loving, tender hearts."

Mary Howitt, "Chamber's Journal," July 11, 1857

Babe Ruth

Appointments

4 Monday

Great educator Mark Hopkins born, 1802

5 Tuesday

Pioneer of religious liberty, Roger Williams, came to America, 1631

6 Wednesday

Baseball legend Babe Ruth born, 1895

7 Thursday

English novelist Charles Dickens born, 1812

8 Friday

Boy Scouts of America chartered, 1910

9 Saturday

US Weather Bureau established, 1870

10 Sunday

Essayist Charles Lamb born, 1775

Diary

Wow! I'm a model. Moelie Bay in 30° weather will never be the same. Had a really good day with J.

St. Valentine's Day

Love is all these things

A Memento of the Day

A Favorite Selection
of Words on Love

A Beloved Person

We, the undersigned, resolve to say
"I love you," each and every day.

21

February						
Sun	Mon	Tue	Wed	Thu	Fri	Sat
					1	2
3	4	5	6	7	8	9
10	11	12	13	14	15	16
17	18	19	20	21	22	23
24	25	26	27	28		

"Great workers are always frequent and orderly, and being possessed of incessant activity, they never lose a moment. They apply their whole mind to what they are about, and, like the hand of a watch, they never stop, although their equal movements in the same day almost escape observation."

"Chamber's Edinburgh Journal," November 29, 1845

Sparking

Born the same day as Thomas Alva Edison, although 45 years before him, author Lydia Child wrote in her poem *"Marius Amid the Ruins of Carthage"* something amazingly prophetic: "Genius hath electric power/ Which earth can never tame,/ Bright suns may scorch and dark clouds lower,/ Its flash is still the same."

Appointments

11 Monday Nonverbal midterm

Novelist Lydia Child born, 1802

12 Tuesday

NAACP founded, on Lincoln's birth centennial, 1909

13 Wednesday

America's 1st magazine, "American Magazine," published, 1741

14 Thursday Hy 252 essay test

St. Valentine's Day
Actress Thelma Ritter born, 1905

15 Friday

Astronomer Galileo Galilei born, 1564

16 Saturday

Ventriloquist Edgar Bergen born, 1903

17 Sunday

National Congress of Mothers founded, 1896

February

Diary

Feel pretty lousy – seem to be catching a cold.
Got my 1st essay test back in History of Eng c/A=B

February

Sun	Mon	Tue	Wed	Thu	Fri	Sat
					1	2
3	4	5	6	7	8	9
10	11	12	13	14	15	16
17	18	19	20	21	22	23
24	25	26	27	28		

"The truth is, I do indulge myself a little the more in pleasure, knowing that this is the proper age of my life to do it; and, out of my observation that most men that do thrive in the world do forget to take pleasure during the time that they are getting their estate, but reserve that till they have got one, and then it is too late...."

Samuel Pepys, Diary, March 10, 1666

"A man would do well to carry a pencil in his pocket and write down the thoughts of the moment. Those that come unsought for are commonly the most valuable, and should be secured, because they seldom return."

Francis Bacon

Appointments
18 Monday   *Presidents Day*   *Guitar virtuoso Andrés Segovia born, 1893*
19 Tuesday   *Shrove Tuesday*   *Astronomer Nicholas Copernicus born, 1473*
20 Wednesday   *Ash Wednesday: Lent begins*   *Chinese New Year—Year of the Ox, 4683*
21 Thursday   *Poet W.H. Auden born, 1907*
22 Friday   *Polish composer Frederic Chopin born, 1810*
23 Saturday   *Great diarist Samuel Pepys born, 1632*   *Hat designer Sally Victor born, 1905*
24 Sunday   *Artist Winslow Homer born, 1836*

February

On Osculation

"Kisses...are like creation, because they are made out of nothing, and are very good. A wag says they are like sermons—they require two heads and an application. An ingenious American grammarian thus conjugates the verb: 'Buss, to kiss; rebus, to kiss again; pluribus, to kiss without regard to number; sillybus, to kiss the hand instead of the lips; blunderbus, to kiss the wrong person; omnibus, to kiss every person in the room; erebus, to kiss in the dark.'"

From Charles Dickens' magazine, "All the Year Round," March 19, 1887

March brings breezes, loud and shrill
To stir the dancing daffodil.
Sarah Coleridge

March

Sun	Mon	Tue	Wed	Thu	Fri	Sat
					1	2
3	4	5	6	7	8	9
10	11	12	13	14	15	16
17	18	19	20	21	22	23
24	25	26	27	28	29	30
31						

Appointments

25 Monday

Beatle George Harrison born, 1943

26 Tuesday

Buffalo Bill (William F. Cody) born, 1846

27 Wednesday

Consumer rights leader Ralph Nader born, 1934

28 Thursday

Dancer Vladislav Nijinsky born, 1890

1 Friday

Red Cross Month & Easter Seal Campaign begin
Singer Dinah Shore born, 1917

2 Saturday

Czechoslovakian composer Bedrich Smetana born, 1824

3 Sunday

Actress Jean Harlow born, 1911

February March

Diary

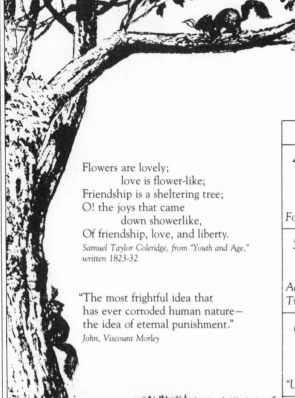

March

Sun	Mon	Tue	Wed	Thu	Fri	Sat
					1	2
3	4	5	6	7	8	9
10	11	12	13	14	15	16
17	18	19	20	21	22	23
24	25	26	27	28	29	30
31						

Flowers are lovely;
            love is flower-like;
Friendship is a sheltering tree;
O! the joys that came
            down showerlike,
Of friendship, love, and liberty.

*Samuel Taylor Coleridge, from "Youth and Age,"
written 1823-32*

"The most frightful idea that
has ever corroded human nature—
the idea of eternal punishment."

John, Viscount Morley

"Do not build me a monument—plant a
tree."

Luther Burbank

Appointments

4 Monday

Football great Knute Rockne born, 1888

5 Tuesday

Actor Rex Harrison born, 1908
Treaty to halt spread of nuclear weapons signed by 43 nations, 1970

6 Wednesday

"Uncle Sam" 1st appeared in cartoon, "Harper's Weekly," 1869

7 Thursday

Purim
Great botanist Luther Burbank born, 1849

8 Friday

Jurist Oliver Wendell Holmes born, 1841

9 Saturday

Mystery writer Mickey Spillane born, 1918

10 Sunday *my birthday - 22*

American organist & composer Dudley Buck born, 1839

March

Diary

'All that glisters', all that shines
out with hope and cheer, with a golden
glow, is not gold. Rather, our pot o'
gold, at the end of the rainbow, is:

A Pretty Irish Poem

Irish or not, today is the day
for the wearin' o' the green!

Shamrock Acrostic

S

H

A

M

R

O

C

K

St. Patrick's Day

What Made Today Memorable

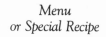

Menu
or Special Recipe

March						
Sun	Mon	Tue	Wed	Thu	Fri	Sat
					1	2
3	4	5	6	7	8	9
10	11	12	13	14	15	16
17	18	19	20	21	22	23
24	25	26	27	28	29	30
31						

Nostalgia

"A floating scent in the air—a scent laden with the memory of a bygone day, a sunset flush in the sky, an old melody borne on the breeze, have been known to bring on an excess of this strange illness, almost unbearable in degree. Reason has little or no effect in subduing its feverish excitement; friendship...cannot turn aside its current; music has no power to soothe its bitterness, nor the distractions of gaiety to rouse it from its melancholy."

From Charles Dickens' magazine, "All the Year Round," February 20, 1886

Appointments

11 Monday

Patron saint of apple orchards, Johnny Appleseed, died, 1847

12 Tuesday

Girl Scouts of America founded, 1912

13 Wednesday

Famed restaurant-proprietor Lorenzo Delmonico born, 1813

14 Thursday

Pioneer librarian Charles Ammi Cutter born, 1837

15 Friday

Ides of March

16 Saturday

Only 32 shares were traded on NY Stock Exchange, 1830

17 Sunday *Charles and Donna's Wedding*

St. Patrick's Day
National Wildlife Week begins

March

Diary

March

Sun	Mon	Tue	Wed	Thu	Fri	Sat
					1	2
3	4	5	6	7	8	9
10	11	12	13	14	15	16
17	18	19	20	21	22	23
24	25	26	27	28	29	30
31						

March

"This solid globe we live upon is called the earth, though it contains in it a great variety of bodies, several whereof are not properly earth; which word, taken in a more limited sense, signifies such parts of this globe as are capable, being exposed to the air, to give rooting and nourishment to plants, so that they may stand and grow in it. With such earth as this, the greatest part of the surface of this globe is covered; and it is as it were the store-house, from whence all living creatures of our world have originally their provisions; for from thence all the plants have their sustenance, and some few animals, and from these all the other animals."

John Locke, An Essay Concerning Human Understanding, 1690

Appointments

18 Monday

Engineer Rudolph Diesel born, 1858

19 Tuesday

6 Englishmen established Massachusetts Bay Colony, 1628

20 Wednesday

Earth Day
Vernal Equinox: Spring begins

21 Thursday

Composer Johann Sebastian Bach born, 1685

22 Friday

1st Indian treaty signed, at Plymouth Colony, 1621

23 Saturday

The incomparable cook Fannie Farmer born, 1857

24 Sunday

Notable, blind hymn-writer Fanny Crosby born, 1820

Diary

March

Sun	Mon	Tue	Wed	Thu	Fri	Sat
					1	2
3	4	5	6	7	8	9
10	11	12	13	14	15	16
17	18	19	20	21	22	23
24	25	26	27	28	29	30
31						

*M*arch

If you are tempted to reveal
A tale to you someone has told
About another, make it pass,
Before you speak, three gates of gold:
These narrow gates. First, "Is it true?"
Then, "Is it needful?" In your mind
Give truthful answer. And the next
Is last and narrowest, "Is it kind?"
And if to reach your lips at last
It passes through these gateways three,
Then you may tell the tale, nor fear
What the result of speech may be.

Beth Day, c. 1855

"The first ingredient in conversation is
truth; the next, good sense; the third, good
humor; and the fourth, wit."
Sir William Temple

Appointments

25 Monday

Annunciation Day
Composer Béla Bartók born, 1881

26 Tuesday

American Practical Navigator author, Nathaniel Bowditch, born, 1773

27 Wednesday

Printmaker for the millions, Nathaniel Currier, born, 1813

28 Thursday

Bandleader Paul Whiteman born, 1891

29 Friday

Ice-jam keeps Niagara Falls from falling for more than a day, 1848

30 Saturday

Actor Warren Beatty born, 1937

31 Sunday

Palm Sunday
Bunsen burner begetter, von Bunsen, born, 1811

Diary

Prayer of Hope

We observed Easter this way

What Flowers Were
in Bloom Today

A Memento of Our Day

Easter

*Today's
weather:*

*Design of a Perfect
Easter Outfit*

*Menu
or
Special Recipe*

Together We Celebrated Easter

April brings the primrose sweet,
Scatters daisies at our feet.
Sarah Coleridge

			April			
Sun	Mon	Tue	Wed	Thu	Fri	Sat
	1	2	3	4	5	6
7	8	9	10	11	12	13
14	15	16	17	18	19	20
21	22	23	24	25	26	27
28	29	30				

"Books are a part of man's prerogative,
In formal ink they thought and voices hold,
That we to them our solitude may give,
And make time present travel that of old.
Our life, fame pierceth longer at the end,
And books it farther backward doth
extend."
Sir Thomas Overbury

"No race can prosper till it learns that there
is as much dignity in tilling a field as in
writing a poem."
Booker Taliaferro Washington, Up From Slavery

Appointments

1 Monday

April Fools Day

2 Tuesday

Librarian, rogue & writer Giacomo Casanova born, 1725

3 Wednesday

Congress passed act establishing 1st coinage mint, 1792

4 Thursday

13 stripes & 13 stars voted by Continental Congress for flag, 1777

5 Friday

Educator, writer, leader Booker T. Washington born, 1856

6 Saturday

Holy Saturday — Blessing of the Animals
Passover begins

7 Sunday

Easter
World Health Day

April

Diary

Now the bloom is on the blade,
In the sun and in the shade.
There is music at our feet,
In the clover, honey-sweet.

Walter Thornbury, March 24, 1860

Old songs are best—how sweet to hear
The strains to home and memory dear!
Old books are best—how tale and rhyme
Float with us down the stream of time!
Clarence Urmy

April

Sun	Mon	Tue	Wed	Thu	Fri	Sat
	1	2	3	4	5	6
7	8	9	10	11	12	13
14	15	16	17	18	19	20
21	22	23	24	25	26	27
28	29	30				

Appointments

8 Monday

Ice skater extraodinaire Sonja Henie born, 1913

9 Tuesday

Animals-in-motion photographer Eadweard Muybridge born, 1830

10 Wednesday

Pulitzer Prize founder/journalist Joseph Pulitzer born, 1847

11 Thursday

Jackie Robinson, 1st major league black, played for Brooklyn Dodgers, 1947

12 Friday

Opera singer Lily Pons born, 1904

13 Saturday

Passover ends
Van Cliburn won Tchaikovsky International Piano Contest in Russia, 1958

14 Sunday

Noah Webster's Dictionary published, 1828

April

Diary

			April			
Sun	Mon	Tue	Wed	Thu	Fri	Sat
	1	2	3	4	5	6
7	8	9	10	11	12	13
14	15	16	17	18	19	20
21	22	23	24	25	26	27
28	29	30				

A Great Pitch

LeRoy "Satchel" Paige, a great baseball pitcher and witty philosopher, once gave six rules by which to lead your life. He began his active career in 1926, and undoubtedly the Roaring Twenties inspired him to advise:

*Avoid fried meats which angry up the blood.

*If your stomach disrupts you, lie down and pacify it with cool thoughts.

*Keep the juices flowing by jangling around gently as you move.

*Go very lightly on the vices, such as carrying on in society. The social ramble ain't restful.

*Avoid running at all times.

*Don't look back. Something might be gaining on you.

"I am a slow walker, but I never walk backwards."
Abraham Lincoln

Appointments

15 Monday

Artist, inventor, remarkable genius Leonardo da Vinci born, 1452

16 Tuesday

Andrew Carnegie established retired university professors' pension, 1905

17 Wednesday

American Academy of Arts and Letters chartered by Congress, 1916

18 Thursday

Patriot Paul Revere made historic "Midnight Ride," 1775

19 Friday

Patriots' Day—Revolutionary War began, 1775

20 Saturday

Andrew Carnegie financed the Hague Peace Palace, in the Netherlands, 1903. If only we had vastly wise (as well as wealthy) men now.

21 Sunday

English novelist Charlotte Bronte born, 1816
English Queen Elizabeth born, 1926

April

Diary

April

Sun	Mon	Tue	Wed	Thu	Fri	Sat
	1	2	3	4	5	6
7	8	9	10	11	12	13
14	15	16	17	18	19	20
21	22	23	24	25	26	27
28	29	30				

If music be the food of love, play on;
Give me excess of it, that, surfeiting,
The appetite may sicken, and so die.
That strain again! it had a dying fall:
O! it came o'er my ear
       like the sweet sound
That breathes upon a bank of violets,
Stealing and giving odour!

William Shakespeare, Twelfth-Night

Appointments

22 Monday

Arbor Day 1st formally observed, in Nebraska, 1872
Earth Day 1st celebrated, 1970

23 Tuesday

The gentle Bard of Avon, William Shakespeare, born, 1564

24 Wednesday

English novelist Anthony Trollope born, 1815

25 Thursday

Singer Ella Fitzgerald born, 1918

26 Friday

Arbor Day in many states
Naturalist/artist John James Audubon born, 1785

27 Saturday

Inventor/artist Samuel F.B. Morse born, 1791

28 Sunday

Daylight Savings begins at 2:00 a.m.: set clocks ahead
Actor Lionel Barrymore born, 1878

April

Diary

May

Sun	Mon	Tue	Wed	Thu	Fri	Sat
			1	2	3	4
5	6	7	8	9	10	11
12	13	14	15	16	17	18
19	20	21	22	23	24	25
26	27	28	29	30	31	

Be Kind to Animals

"We are bound to study the means of preserving the health and administering to the wants of animals, by all those precepts in 'Holy Writ,' which recommend kindness to them, and protection from outrage and oppression. A portion of the humane spirit of those precepts has pervaded all countries, and descended in a particular manner to the nations of the East."

"American Agriculturist," September 1846

May brings flocks of pretty lambs
Skipping by their fleecy dams.
Sarah Coleridge

Appointments

29 Monday

Jazz noble Duke Ellington born, 1899

30 Tuesday

Queen Juliana of Holland born, 1909

1 Wednesday

May Day & Law Day
Singer Kate Smith born, 1909

2 Thursday

Singer/actor Bing Crosby born, 1904

3 Friday

National Public Radio began programming, 1971

4 Saturday

Kentucky Derby
4 students killed by National Guards during anti-war protest, 1970

5 Sunday

Be Kind to Animals Week begins
National Family Week begins

April May

Diary

Mother's Day

Our Special Name for Mother

Mother's Maiden Name and Birthday

Grandmothers' Maiden Names and Birthdays

Great-Grandmothers' Maiden Names and Birthdays

Mother's Most Memorable Saying

Mother's Most Memorable Habit

Why Mother is Lovable

A Memento or Photo of the Day

May

Sun	Mon	Tue	Wed	Thu	Fri	Sat
			1	2	3	4
5	6	7	8	9	10	11
12	13	14	15	16	17	18
19	20	21	22	23	24	25
26	27	28	29	30	31	

On Enthusiasm

"He that would seriously set upon the search of truth, ought in the first place to prepare his mind with a love of it. For he that loves it not, will not take much pains to get it, nor be much concened when he misses it. There is nobody in the commonwealth of learning, who does not profess himself a lover of truth."

John Locke, An Essay Concerning Human Understanding, *1690*

Appointments

6 Monday

North Pole discoverer Robert E. Peary born, 1856

7 Tuesday

Poet and Librarian of Congress Archibald MacLeish born, 1892

8 Wednesday

Explorer Hernando de Soto arrived at Mississippi River, near Memphis, 1541

9 Thursday

Abolitionist John Brown born, 1800

10 Friday

Dancer Fred Astaire born, 1899

11 Saturday

Composer Irving Berlin born, 1888
"Miss Marple" actress Margaret Rutherford born, 1892

12 Sunday

Mothers' Day
Rogation Sunday

May

Diary

May

Sun	Mon	Tue	Wed	Thu	Fri	Sat
			1	2	3	4
5	6	7	8	9	10	11
12	13	14	15	16	17	18
19	20	21	22	23	24	25
26	27	28	29	30	31	

"The grass next door may look greener but it's just as hard to cut."
Saying on advertising card, 1880s

The Revenues of the Mind
"The ear and the eye are the mind's receivers; but the tongue is only busied in expending the treasure received. If, therefore, the revenues of the mind be uttered as fast or faster than they are received, it cannot be but that the mind must needs be bare, and can never lay up for purchase. But if the receivers take in still with no utterance, the mind may soon grow a burden to itself, and unprofitable to others. I will not lay up too much, and utter nothing, lest I be covetous; nor spend much, and store up little, lest I be prodigal and poor."
Bishop Hall, quoted in "Chambers Journal," July 5, 1845

Appointments
13 Monday
Light opera composer Arthur Sullivan born, 1842 *1st Mothers' Day observance, 1934*
14 Tuesday
Benefactor John D. Rockefeller gave $100,000,000 fund to promote "the well-being of mankind thruout the world," 1913
15 Wednesday
Photographer Richard Avedon born, 1923
16 Thursday
Ascension *Novelist Honoré de Balzac born, 1799*
17 Friday
Frihesdag—or Independence Day—in Norway, commemorates 1814 constitution
18 Saturday
Puritans compelled Massachusetts to allow only church members to vote, 1631
19 Sunday
Philanthropist Johns Hopkins born, 1795

May

Diary

May
Sun Mon Tue Wed Thu Fri Sat
1 2 3 4
5 6 7 8 9 10 11
12 13 14 15 16 17 18
19 20 21 22 23 24 25
26 27 28 29 30 31

"It is a great thing to start life with a small number of really good books which are your very own."

Sir Arthur Conan Doyle, in Through the Magic Door

Captain Charles A. Lindbergh flew from New York to Paris in 33 hours, 29 minutes, 30 seconds, landing to the thankful cheers of well-wishers, on May 20, 1927. He was the first to make the transatlantic flight, solo and non-stop.

Appointments
20 Monday   *Victoria Day*   *Actor James Stewart born, 1908*
21 Tuesday   *American Red Cross founded, by Clara Barton, 1881*
22 Wednesday   *Sir Arthur Conan Doyle, creator of Sherlock Holmes, born, 1859*
23 Thursday   *Pirate Captain Kidd, 1st employed to catch pirates, executed, 1701*
24 Friday   *"Washington Crossing the Delaware" painter, Emanuel Leutze, born, 1816*
25 Saturday   *Belmont Stakes*   *Poet Ralph Waldo Emerson born, 1803*
26 Sunday   *Pentecost or Whitsunday*   *Shavuoth—Feast of Weeks*

May

Diary

*Today's
weather:*

What We Want to Remember

Words on Memory and Love

Memorial Day

What Special Thing Was Done Today

A Memento of the Day

June brings tulips, lilies, roses,
Fills the children's hands with posies.
Sarah Coleridge

The Making of the
Humming-Bird, from an
Indian Legend

A bird and a bee, in the fresh April
weather,/ Sailed blithely to meet the first
summer together./ 'Twas a very small bird,
and a very large bee,/ And they talked as
they flew, and they couldn't agree/ As to
which of the two should first greet the
sweet summer,/ The bright-plumaged bird
or the busy young hummer./ All at once a
black wind-storm dropped down from the
skies,/ And it took this small quarreling
pair by surprise./ It whirled them about,
until, drenched and half-dead,/ They both
tumbled into a violet-bed./ When the sun
shone again—(this is what I have heard)—/
That bird was a bee, and that bee was a
bird;/ and only one creature went
humming away,/ Dipping into the flower-
cups, that fresh April day.
Annie A. Preston, "St. Nicholas," August 1880

June						
Sun	Mon	Tue	Wed	Thu	Fri	Sat
						1
2	3	4	5	6	7	8
9	10	11	12	13	14	15
16	17	18	19	20	21	22
23	24	25	26	27	28	29
30						

Appointments
27 Monday *Memorial Day* *Modern dance pioneer Isadora Duncan born, 1878*
28 Tuesday   *The Dionne Quintuplets born, celebrated the world over, 1934*
29 Wednesday   *Stravinsky's ballet "The Rite of Spring" premiered, 1913*
30 Thursday   *Memorial Day—Decoration Day—1st observed, 1868*
31 Friday   *Leaves of Grass poet Walt Whitman born, 1819*
1 Saturday *Adopt-a-Cat Month begins* *Actress Marilyn Monroe born, 1926*
2 Sunday *Pat-a-Cat Day* *Johnny Weissmuller—Tarzan personified—born, 1904*

May June

Diary

June

Sun	Mon	Tue	Wed	Thu	Fri	Sat
						1
2	3	4	5	6	7	8
9	10	11	12	13	14	15
16	17	18	19	20	21	22
23	24	25	26	27	28	29
30						

The Future

"Nothing worth doing is completed in our lifetime; therefore we must be saved by hope. Nothing true or beautiful or good makes complete sense in any immediate context of history; therefore we must be saved by faith. Nothing we do, however virtuous, can be accomplished alone; therefore we are saved by love. No virtuous act is quite as virtuous from the standpoint of our friend or foe as from our standpoint. Therefore we must be saved by the final form of love, which is forgiveness."

Reinhold Niebuhr, The Irony of American History, *1952*

"History does not reveal its alternatives."

Eric Severeid, January 15, 1983

Appointments

3 Monday

Actor Tony Curtis born, 1925

4 Tuesday

1st NYC to San Francisco through train took 83 hours, 34 minutes, 1876

5 Wednesday

*World Environment Day
UN Conference on the Human Environment opened, 1972*

6 Thursday

World's 1st drive-in theatre — Camden NJ — opened, 1933

7 Friday

Boone Day: pioneer Daniel Boone 1st saw Kentucky, 1769

8 Saturday

Ives W. McGaffey given patent for vacuum cleaner, 1869

9 Sunday

Race Unity Day

June

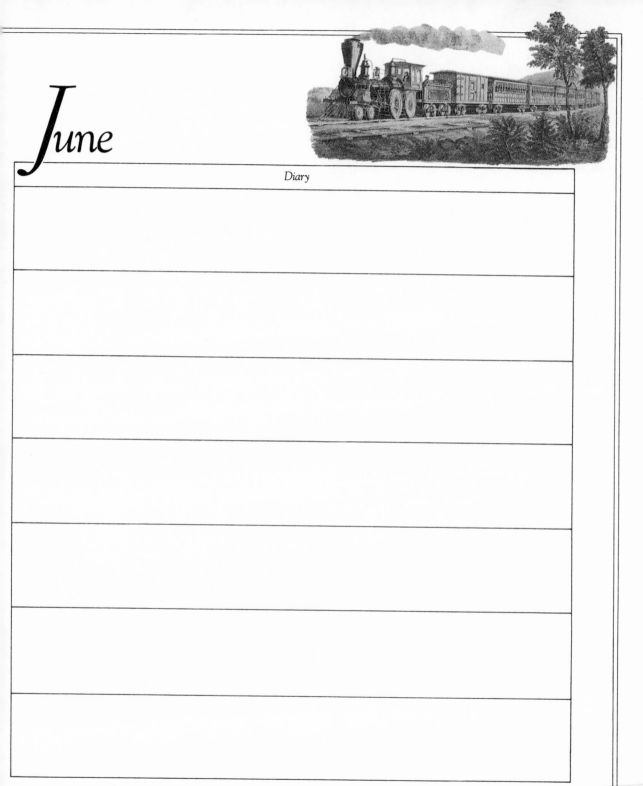

Diary

Today's weather:

Our Special Name for Father

Father's Full Name and Birthday

Father's Most Memorable Saying

Grandfathers' Full Names and Birthdays

Great-Grandfathers' Full Names and Birthdays

Father's Day

Why Father is Lovable

A Memento or Photo of the Day

June

Sun	Mon	Tue	Wed	Thu	Fri	Sat
						1
2	3	4	5	6	7	8
9	10	11	12	13	14	15
16	17	18	19	20	21	22
23	24	25	26	27	28	29
30						

"Men that have senses cannot choose but receive some ideas by them; and if they have memory, they cannot but retain some of them; and if they have any distinguishing faculty, cannot but perceive the agreement or disagreement of some of them one with another: as he that has eyes, if he will open them by day, cannot but see some objects, and perceive a difference in them. But though a man with his eyes open in the light, cannot but see; yet there be certain objects, which he may choose whether he will turn his eyes to; there may be in his reach a book containing pictures and discourses, capable to delight or instruct him, which yet he may never have the will to open, never take the pains to look into."

John Locke, An Essay Concerning Human Understanding, *1690*

Appointments
10 Monday *Actress Judy Garland born, 1922* *Alcoholics Anonymous founded, 1935*
11 Tuesday *1st female member of Congress, Jeannette Rankin, born, 1880*
12 Wednesday *Diarist Anne Frank born, 1929*
13 Thursday *Poet/dramatist William Butler Yates born, 1865*
14 Friday *Harriet Beecher Stowe,* Uncle Tom's Cabin *author, born, 1811*
15 Saturday *Statesman/inventor/printer Benjamin Franklin flew kite in a lightning storm to study electricity, 1752*
16 Sunday *Fathers' Day—1st observed nationally in 1934* *The World Court organized, 1920*

June

Diary

			June			
Sun	Mon	Tue	Wed	Thu	Fri	Sat
						1
2	3	4	5	6	7	8
9	10	11	12	13	14	15
16	17	18	19	20	21	22
23	24	25	26	27	28	29
30						

Why We Must Climb Mountains
Mountains interposed
Make enemies of nations, who had else
Like kindred drops been mingled into one.
William Cowper, in "The Task"

Appointments

17 Monday

Author John Hersey born, 1914

18 Tuesday

Why climb Everest? "Because it's there" mountaineer George Mallory born, 1886

19 Wednesday

Wallis Simpson, who became Duchess of Windsor, born, 1896

20 Thursday

Country guitarist Chet Atkins born, 1924

21 Friday

Summer Solstice: Summer begins
US Constitution ratified by required 9th state, New Hampshire, 1788

22 Saturday

Author/aviator Anne Morrow Lindbergh born, 1907

23 Sunday

Humorist/writer Irvin S. Cobb born, 1876

June

Diary

June

Sun	Mon	Tue	Wed	Thu	Fri	Sat
						1
2	3	4	5	6	7	8
9	10	11	12	13	14	15
16	17	18	19	20	21	22
23	24	25	26	27	28	29
30						

"A persuasion that we shall overcome any difficulties that we meet with in the sciences, seldom fails to carry us through them. Nobody knows the strength of his mind, and the force of steady and regular application, till he has tried. This is certain, he that sets out upon weak legs, will not only go farther, but grow stronger than one, who with a vigorous constitution and firm limbs, only sits still."

John Locke, An Essay Concerning Human Understanding, *1690*

Appointments

24 Monday

Boxing champion Jack Dempsey born, 1895

25 Tuesday

Wage and Hours Act—44 hours a week, 20¢ an hour—enacted, 1938

26 Wednesday

Discovery Day in Newfoundland
Author Pearl S. Buck born, 1892

27 Thursday

Blind and deaf author/advocate Helen Keller born, 1880

28 Friday

Painter Peter Paul Rubens born, 1577. The only artist whose name is an adjective for women!

29 Saturday

Panama Canal engineer George W. Goethals born, 1858

30 Sunday

Charles Blondin—French aerialist—walked rope over Niagara Falls, 1859

June

Diary

Fourth of July

Today's weather:

Freedoms to Treasure

A Song for the Fourth

Sung to the tune of _____

*Picnic Menu
or
Favorite Recipe*

A Memento of the Day

July						
Sun	Mon	Tue	Wed	Thu	Fri	Sat
	1	2	3	4	5	6
7	8	9	10	11	12	13
14	15	16	17	18	19	20
21	22	23	24	25	26	27
28	29	30	31			

Hot July brings cooling showers
Apricots and gillyflowers.
Sarah Coleridge

Let Freedom Ring

"...Let freedom ring from the prodigious hilltops of New Hampshire; let freedom ring from the mighty mountains of New York; let freedom ring from the heights of the Alleghenies of Pennsylvania; let freedom ring from the snow-capped Rockies of Colorado; let freedom ring from the curvaceous slopes of California. But not only that, let freedom ring from the Stone Mountains of Georgia; let freedom ring from Lookout Mountain of Tennessee; let freedom ring from every hill and molehill in Mississippi—from every mountainside let freedom ring.

"And when this happens, when we allow freedom to ring—when we let it ring from every village and every hamlet, from every state and every city, we will be able to speed up that day when all of God's children, black men and white men, Jews and Gentiles, Protestants and Catholics will be able to join hands and sing in the words of the old Negro spiritual, 'Free at last, free at last, thank God Almighty, we're free at last.'"

Rev. Dr. Martin Luther King Jr., "I Have a Dream" speech in Washington DC, August 28, 1963

Appointments
1 Monday   *Canada Day*   *1st US postage stamp, 1847*
2 Tuesday   *1st Black Supreme Court Justice, Thurgood Marshall, born, 1908*
3 Wednesday   *Beginning of "Dog Days"*
4 Thursday   *Independence Day*
5 Friday   *David G. Farragut, American navy's 1st admiral, born, 1801*
6 Saturday   *Naval patriot John Paul Jones born, 1747*
7 Sunday   *Kings College, later Columbia, opened NYC, 1754*

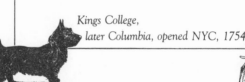

July

Diary

"I base most of my fashion taste on what doesn't itch."
Gilda Radner

"A true critick ought to dwell rather upon excellencies than imperfections, to discover the concealed beauties of a writer, and communicate to the world such things as are worth their observation."
Joseph Addison, "The Spectator," February 2, 1712

July

Sun	Mon	Tue	Wed	Thu	Fri	Sat
	1	2	3	4	5	6
7	8	9	10	11	12	13
14	15	16	17	18	19	20
21	22	23	24	25	26	27
28	29	30	31			

Appointments

8 Monday

1st US passport issued—to Francis Barre, 1796

9 Tuesday

Sewing machine inventor Elias Howe born, 1819

10 Wednesday

Pioneer of electricity Nikola Tesla born, 1856

11 Thursday

Floating iron swimming pool moored on the River Thames, London, 1875

12 Friday

English potter Josiah Wedgwood born, 1730

13 Saturday

Critic Bosley Crowther born, 1905

14 Sunday

Film-maker Ingmar Bergman born, 1918

July

Diary

Oil Cloth
From Woolly & Co.
N.Y.

To J Smithers
Drylands
N.J.

№ 2

			July			
Sun	Mon	Tue	Wed	Thu	Fri	Sat
	1	2	3	4	5	6
7	8	9	10	11	12	13
14	15	16	17	18	19	20
21	22	23	24	25	26	27
28	29	30	31			

Rash Opinions

We judge too rashly both of men and things,/ Giving to-day's opinions on the morrow/ Utter denial, while we strive to borrow/ Hollow apologies that—like the wings/ Of butterflies—show many colours. Sorrow/ Hideth its tears, and we disclaim its presence/ Where it hath deepest root; Hate softly brings/ A smile, which we account Love's sweetest essence;/ Simplicity seems Art; and Art we deem/ White-hearted Innocence—misjudging ever/ Of all we see! Let us, then, grant esteem,/ Or grudge it with precaution only; never/ Forgetting that rash haste right judgment mars:/ What men count but as clouds may prove bright stars.

Calder Campbell, in "Chamber's Journal," March 3, 1849

Appointments

15 Monday

Jazz pianist Errol Garner born, 1921

16 Tuesday

Kissing banned to prevent plague's spread, in England, 1439

17 Wednesday

Comedienne Phyllis Diller born, 1921

18 Thursday

Comedian Red Skelton born, 1913

19 Friday

1st women's rights convention held, 1848

20 Saturday

1st all-star baseball game—between two unpaid amateur clubs—played, 1858. New York: 22, Brooklyn: 18.

21 Sunday

Marshall Medium is the Message McLuhan born, 1911

July

Diary

July

Sun	Mon	Tue	Wed	Thu	Fri	Sat
	1	2	3	4	5	6
7	8	9	10	11	12	13
14	15	16	17	18	19	20
21	22	23	24	25	26	27
28	29	30	31			

Appointments

22 Monday

Sculptor of mobiles Alexander Calder born, 1989

23 Tuesday

1st ice cream cone made, 1904 (The flavor vanilla, the blessing mixed?)

24 Wednesday

Antoine de la Mothe Cadillac landed at Detroit's site, 1701

25 Thursday

Puerto Rican Constitution Day

26 Friday

Playwright/vegetarian George Bernard Shaw born, 1856

27 Saturday

Cyrus W. Field at last connected Europe and America with electric telegraph. Steamship dragged cable Ireland to Newfoundland, 1866

28 Sunday

Volunteers of America founder Ballington Booth born, 1859

"The great secret, Eliza, is not having bad manners or good manners or any other particular sort of manners, but having the same manner for all human souls; in short, behaving as if you were in Heaven, where there are no third-class carriages, and one soul is as good as another."

George Bernard Shaw, Pygmalion, Act V

"Every achievement is but a camping place for the night."

Saying on an 1880's trade card

July

Diary

August

Sun	Mon	Tue	Wed	Thu	Fri	Sat
				1	2	3
4	5	6	7	8	9	10
11	12	13	14	15	16	17
18	19	20	21	22	23	24
25	26	27	28	29	30	31

August brings sheaves of corn,
Then the harvest home is borne.
Sarah Coleridge

Composer Franz Liszt's advice to piano players was "Eat well and walk much."

Appointments

29 Monday

Novelist Booth Tarkington born, 1869

30 Tuesday

Baseball's Casey Stengel born, 1891

31 Wednesday

Tennis champion Evonne Goolagong born, 1951

1 Thursday

Moby Dick *author Herman Melville born, 1819*

2 Friday

America's 1st street mailboxes set up, in Boston, 1858

3 Saturday

Lake Victoria, source of the Nile, discovered in Africa, 1858

4 Sunday

Poet Percy Bysshe Shelley born, 1792

July $\mathcal{A}$ugust

Diary

August

Sun	Mon	Tue	Wed	Thu	Fri	Sat
				1	2	3
4	5	6	7	8	9	10
11	12	13	14	15	16	17
18	19	20	21	22	23	24
25	26	27	28	29	30	31

Appointments

5 Monday

North America's 1st English colony founded, Newfoundland, 1583

6 Tuesday

Comedienne Lucille Ball born, 1911

7 Wednesday

Statesman/Nobel Peace Prize winner Ralph Bunche born, 1904

8 Thursday

Newspaperman Charles A. Dana born, 1819

9 Friday

Great angler/author Izaak Walton born, 1593

10 Saturday

Greenwich (England) Observatory, world's time regulator, began construction, 1675

11 Sunday

Art collector Joseph Hirshhorn born, 1899

"Sir Henry Wotton was a most dear lover and a frequent practiser of the Art of Angling; of which he would say, ' 'Twas an employment for his idle time, which was then not idly spent, a rest to his mind, a cheerer of his spirits, a diverter of sadness, a calmer of unquiet thoughts, a moderator of passions, a procurer of contentedness."
Izaak Walton, The Compleat Angler

$\mathcal{A}$ugust

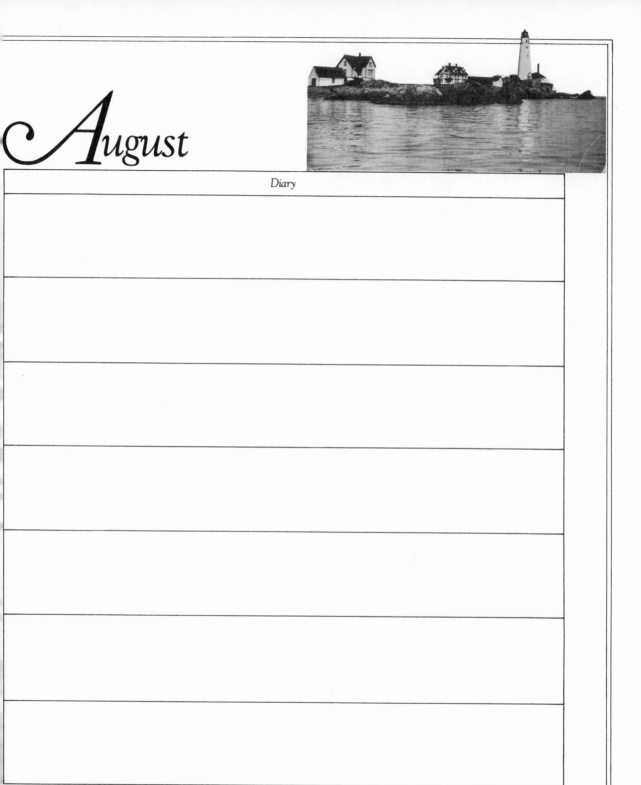

Diary

August

Sun	Mon	Tue	Wed	Thu	Fri	Sat
				1	2	3
4	5	6	7	8	9	10
11	12	13	14	15	16	17
18	19	20	21	22	23	24
25	26	27	28	29	30	31

Letter on a Country Week-End

"...They have such *breakfasts*, well you know my weakness, all those *rows* of dishes, I do *venerate* having about 9 things to choose from, don't you, well, when I tell you that there was kipper and kedgeree and fried fish and bacon and eggs, and bacon and tomato and scrambled eggs, and the *most* Elysian kidneys...and...porridge and... *celestial* ham and strawberries...I could have spent the *entire* morning just *flittering* like a humming-bird from dish to dish, simply toying with them of *course*...."

A.P. Herbert, Topsy, 1930

Appointments

12 Monday

Baseball great Christy Mathewson born, 1880

13 Tuesday

William Caxton, 1st English printer, born, 1422. He believed in books the "common man" could read, not just Latin scholars.

14 Wednesday

Circus entrepeneur John Ringling North born, 1903

15 Thursday

Assumption Day
Botanist John Torrey born, 1796

16 Friday

Gold discovered in Alaska, Yukon Province, 1896

17 Saturday

Pioneer Davy Crockett born, 1786

18 Sunday

America's 1st ocean exploration fleet sailed, from Norwalk VA, 1838

August

Diary

August

Sun	Mon	Tue	Wed	Thu	Fri	Sat
				1	2	3
4	5	6	7	8	9	10
11	12	13	14	15	16	17
18	19	20	21	22	23	24
25	26	27	28	29	30	31

Appointments

19 Monday

Humorist Ogden Nash born, 1902

20 Tuesday

Poet Robert Herrick born, 1591

21 Wednesday

Jazz musician Count Basie born, 1906

22 Thursday

1st successful steamboat in America, clocked 3 mph, 1787
"Spirit of '76" painter Archibald M. Willard born, 1836

23 Friday

Spoon River Anthology author Edgar Lee Masters born, 1868

24 Saturday

President Lincoln received 1st coast-to-coast telegram, 1861

25 Sunday

National Park Service founded, 1916

Dream of a Spelling Bee
Menageries where sluth hounds caracole,/
Where jaguar phalanx and phlegmatic gnu/
Fright ptarmigan and kestrels cheek by
jowl/ With peewit and precocious
cockatoo./

Gaunt seneschals, in crotchety cockades,/
With seine net trawl for porpoise in
lagoons;/ While scullions gauge erratic
escapades/ Of madrepores in water-logged
galleons./

Flamboyant triptychs groined with gherkins
green,/ In reckless fracas with coquettish
bream,/ Ecstatic gargoyles, with grotesque
chagrin,/ Garnish the gruesome nightmare
of my dream.

*Quoted in "Record of the Year," March 7, 1876.
Originally from "Punch"*

August

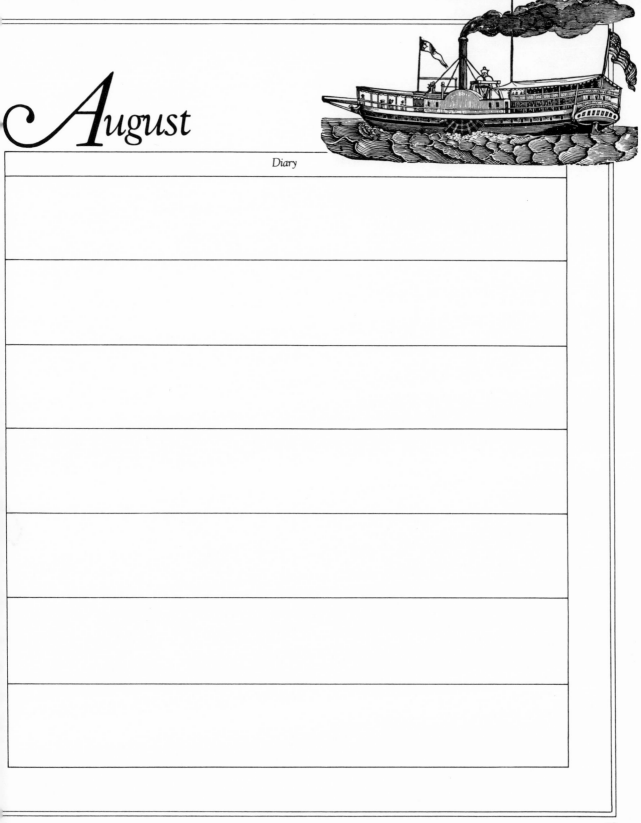

Diary

August

Sun	Mon	Tue	Wed	Thu	Fri	Sat
				1	2	3
4	5	6	7	8	9	10
11	12	13	14	15	16	17
18	19	20	21	22	23	24
25	26	27	28	29	30	31

Warm September makes us mellow,
Begins to turn leaves red and yellow.
Grace McFarland

"A professor can never better distinguish himself in his work than by encouraging a clever pupil, for the true discoverers are among them, as comets amongst the stars."
Carl Linnaeus

Appointments

26 Monday

Discovery Day in the Yukon
19th Amendment, granting women right to vote, 1920

27 Tuesday

"Oil! We've struck it!", 69' down near Titusville PA; US's 1st oilwell, 1859

28 Wednesday

Actor Charles "What a Voice" Boyer born, 1889

29 Thursday

Jurist Oliver Wendell Holmes born, 1809

30 Friday

Victim of the Puritan state, Anne Hutchinson, banished for discussing sermons with friends, 1637

31 Saturday

Worst known earthquake east of the Mississippi, 1886

1 Sunday

Tarzan's *author Edgar Rice Burroughs born, 1875*

August *September*

Diary

What Is a Labor of Love?

The Most Interesting Sight Seen Today

$Labor$ Day

Today's weather:

A Memento of the Day

Recipe for a Picnic

September

Sun	Mon	Tue	Wed	Thu	Fri	Sat
1	2	3	4	5	6	7
8	9	10	11	12	13	14
15	16	17	18	19	20	21
22	23	24	25	26	27	28
29	30					

"In looking round upon the busy walks of life, we find that not a few consist of this Go-along kind of people. They will listen attentively to your benevolent projects; they will express their approbation of your principles of action; they will profess unqualified admiration of your mode of proceeding, and their cordial sympathy with the end you have in view; but immediately you solicit their...aid, they shrink from your appeal, and endeavour to shuffle you off by protests of inability, or by plausibly insisting that they shall require time to consider of it; and endeavour to hide their indolence or parsimony under the plea of waiting to see 'how it will work.' ...Go-alongs sigh over the ignorance and wickedness of the world, bidding you good speed...but do not dream of putting a finger to the work."
"Chamber's Edinburgh Journal," October 11, 1845

Appointments

2 Monday

Labor Day

3 Tuesday

Skyscraper architect Louis Sullivan born, 1856

4 Wednesday

1st transcontinental TV broadcast, 1951

5 Thursday

Nielsen Rating founder/marketing expert Arthur Nielsen born, 1923

6 Friday

Social welfare pioneer Jane Addams born, 1860

7 Saturday

Beloved naïve artist, Grandma Moses, born, 1860

8 Sunday

Grandparents Day
Actor—Inspector Clouseau, most memorably—Peter Sellers born, 1925

September

In two little words all the difference lies,
I always say "come," and you always say "go.' . . .
You say "go" to your man, as you lay in your bed,
I say, "Come, Jack, with me,"
            and I see the work done."

R.S. Sharpe, "Come and Go"

Diary

September

Sun	Mon	Tue	Wed	Thu	Fri	Sat
1	2	3	4	5	6	7
8	9	10	11	12	13	14
15	16	17	18	19	20	21
22	23	24	25	26	27	28
29	30					

Surprise

In 1978, the editor's father bought a cord of applewood logs from a Charlottesville, Virginia neighbor. While stacking the higgledy-piggledy pile, Franklin saw something glint in the sun. It wasn't a nail but a gold class ring, embedded in the wood, with only the monogrammed shield, "G**M**S", and the date, 1922, showing. Coincidentally, the letters and date suited Franklin's Memphis grammar school graduation. A tree man working in the yard that day looked closely at the ring and decided "It wasn't drove in, it must have growed in." Unclaimed, though advertised, the ring and its harboring log are part of the cabinet of curiosities in the Franklin home.

In 1980, a University of Virginia graduate was fishing on Chesapeake Bay. A storm came up, he grabbed for the boom, and his UVa class ring flew off into 30 feet of water. Diving the next day proved futile.

In 1982, another UVa grad was standing behind a Charlottesville diner, next to a fishmonger's that had closed months before. He saw something shining on the ground: a class ring. It was the ring lost two years before in the Bay, and was identified through the engravings inside the ring.

"I find things on the ground all the time," says Franklin; "I'm always picking things up off the ground," says the finder of the fish-food ring.

Prospecting in Charlottesville might not always be so lucky, but if you've lost a class ring in the last, say, 60 years, you may want to go *there* to look for it...eyes down, of course.

Appointments

9 Monday

1st giant panda born in captivity, in China, 1963

10 Tuesday

Elias Howe's sewing machine patented, 1846

11 Wednesday

Short story writer William Sidney Porter—O. Henry—born, 1862

12 Thursday

Newspaperman/critic H.L. Mencken born, 1880

13 Friday

Henry Hudson sailed into mouth of river later named for him, 1609

14 Saturday

Feminist/nurse Margaret Sanger born, 1883

15 Sunday

Greatly-loved mystery-writer Agatha Christie born, 1890

September

September

Sun	Mon	Tue	Wed	Thu	Fri	Sat
1	2	3	4	5	6	7
8	9	10	11	12	13	14
15	16	17	18	19	20	21
22	23	24	25	26	27	28
29	30					

"One aspect of vanity...is the pride some people take in their walking powers. It is astonishing what distances some of our friends cover when they go for a 'good country walk'; although at times...their 'must have been quite twenty miles' often proves, much to their chagrin, a bare dozen. Doubtless, to one unaccustomed to walking the distance traversed seems much greater than it really is, especially if there has been little to attract attention or enliven the road. A pleasant companion shortens the road wonderfully, and cheerful spirits are of great assistance in a pedestrian tour."

From Charles Dickens' magazine, "All the Year Round,"
April 28, 1887

"No place affords a more striking conviction of the vanity of human hopes, than a public library."

Samuel Johnson, "The Rambler," March 23, 1751

Appointments

16 Monday

Rosh Hashanah begins: Jewish New Year 5746

17 Tuesday

Constitution Day—US Constitution signed, 1787

18 Wednesday

Author Samuel Johnson born, 1709

19 Thursday

Illustrator Arthur Rackham born, 1867

20 Friday

Author Upton Sinclair born, 1878

21 Saturday

Macadam road surfacing inventor, John McAdam, born, 1756

22 Sunday

Autumnal Equinox: Fall begins
Boxer Ingemar Johansson born, 1932

September

Diary

About now you'll begin to be able to see—with a backyard telescope—this once-in-a-lifetime celestial legend. It'll perk up in November, but be brightest in January and March 1986. Best view: from Australia.

(See November 8.)

September						
Sun	Mon	Tue	Wed	Thu	Fri	Sat
1	2	3	4	5	6	7
8	9	10	11	12	13	14
15	16	17	18	19	20	21
22	23	24	25	26	27	28
29	30					

Appointments

23 Monday

Eclectic Reader *author/educator William McGuffey born, 1800*

24 Tuesday

Author F. Scott Fitzgerald—The Great Gatsby—born, 1896

25 Wednesday

Yom Kippur—Day of Atonement
Yosemite National Park established, 1890

26 Thursday

Composer George Gershwin born, 1898

27 Friday

Woman in auto, smoking cigarette, arrested in NYC, 1905

28 Saturday

Actress Brigitte Bardot born, 1934

29 Sunday

Michaelmas Day

Premature Frost

"While it is customary to become lugubrious over the approaching end of the outdoor flower season, I am unable to grow *triste* about it. I welcome any premature frost. By the end of September one becomes surfeited with garden beauty. Since the early days of Spring our emotions have been tugged at, and now, with Autumn at hand and much beauty still to come from coloring leaves and harlequin countryside, emotions are almost tugged out. So come quick, sharp early frost! Obliterate some of this beauty! Clear the decks for the majesty of Autumn!"

Richardson Wright, The Gardener's Bed-Book, *1929*

September

Diary

September

Sun	Mon	Tue	Wed	Thu	Fri	Sat
1	2	3	4	5	6	7
8	9	10	11	12	13	14
15	16	17	18	19	20	21
22	23	24	25	26	27	28
29	30					

Appointments

Crisp October sees the squirrel
Gathering nuts for winter's burrow.
Grace McFarland

30 Monday

Feast Day of St. Jerome, scholar/librarian

1 Tuesday

Actress Julie Andrews born, 1935

2 Wednesday

Comedian Groucho Marx born, 1895

3 Thursday

Historian/author George Bancroft born, 1800

4 Friday

Actor Buster Keaton born, 1896

5 Saturday

Film-maker Joshua Logan born, 1908

6 Sunday

Explorer—on the "Kon Tiki" notably—Thor Heyerdahl born, 1914

The stately ship is seen no more,
The fragile skiff attains the shore;
And while the great and wise decay,
And all their trophies pass away,
Some sudden thought,
      some careless rhyme,
Still floats above the wrecks of Time.
William Edward Hartpole Lecky, "On an Old Song"

September October

Diary

October

Sun	Mon	Tue	Wed	Thu	Fri	Sat
		1	2	3	4	5
6	7	8	9	10	11	12
13	14	15	16	17	18	19
20	21	22	23	24	25	26
27	28	29	30	31		

"Excess severity is not the path to order. On the contrary, it is the path to the bomb."
John, Viscount Morley, 1838–1923

"I am often called an optimist, and so I am; but perhaps not in the popular meaning of the word. When a worldly wise man calls a person an optimist, he usually regards him with intellectual contempt, just as the elaborate courtesy toward women in the age of chivalry thinly disguised a cynically sensual attitude. Optimism is associated in many minds either with ignorance of life or mental inferiority; and when certain persons call others optimists, look out for them!...

"A true optimist is one who recognizes the sorrows, worries, drawbacks, misfortunes of life, its injustice and inequalities. But while seeing these things, the optimist believes that no matter how strong error may be, truth in the long run will triumph, even though it may not be our truth."
William Lyon Phelps, Essays on Things, *1931*

Appointments

7 Monday

Universal Childrens Day

8 Tuesday

Chicago Fire began, 1871. Mrs. O'Leary said her cow didn't kick over the lantern, but it was her cowshed where it all started.

9 Wednesday

Leif Ericsson Day

10 Thursday

Actress Helen Hayes born, 1900

11 Friday

Founder of the YMCA, Sir George Williams, born, 1821

12 Saturday

1st celebration of Columbus' discovery of America, in NYC, 1792

13 Sunday

Actor Yves Montand born, 1921

October

Diary

October

Sun	Mon	Tue	Wed	Thu	Fri	Sat
		1	2	3	4	5
6	7	8	9	10	11	12
13	14	15	16	17	18	19
20	21	22	23	24	25	26
27	28	29	30	31		

Well-well, the world must turn
        upon its axis,
And all mankind turn with it,
        heads or tails,
And live and die, make love
        and pay our taxes,
And as the veering winds shift,
        shift our sails;
The king commands us, and
        the doctor quacks us,
The priest instructs, and so
        our lifes exhales,
A little breath, love, wine,
        ambition, fame,
Fighting, devotion, dust,—
        perhaps a name.

Lord Byron, "Don Juan"

Appointments

14 Monday

Columbus Day—Discovery Day
Canadian Thanksgiving Day (see page 120)

15 Tuesday

Ether 1st used, in Boston, 1846

16 Wednesday

Playwright Eugene O'Neill born, 1888

17 Thursday

NYC boarding-housekeepers voted a 4-prune breakfast for boarders, 1824

18 Friday

Actress Melina Mercouri born, 1925

19 Saturday

1st balloon wedding, over Cincinnati, 1874

20 Sunday

Baseball great Mickey Mantle born, 1931

October

Diary

October

Sun	Mon	Tue	Wed	Thu	Fri	Sat
		1	2	3	4	5
6	7	8	9	10	11	12
13	14	15	16	17	18	19
20	21	22	23	24	25	26
27	28	29	30	31		

E-ri-e

We were forty miles from Albany
Forget it, I never shall.
What a terrible storm we had one night,
On the E-ri-e Canal.

Chorus:
Oh the E-ri-e was a-rising,
And the gin was a-getting low.
And I scarcely think we'll get a drink,
Till we get to Buffalo,
Till we get to Buffalo.

Mary had a little lamb,
  Its fleece was white as snow,
And everywhere that Mary went
  The lamb was sure to go;
He followed her to school one day,
  That was against the rule;
It made the children laugh and play
  To see a lamb in school.

Sarah Josepha Hale, September 1830

Appointments
21 Monday   *Poet Will Carleton born, 1845*
22 Tuesday   *Composer/pianist Franz Liszt born, 1811*
23 Wednesday   *Writer Gore Vidal born, 1925*
24 Thursday   *"Mary Had a Little Lamb" author, Sarah Hale, born 1788*   *The United Nations chartered, 1945*
25 Friday   *Women bought 1st nylon stockings, 1940*
26 Saturday   *The Erie Canal—Hudson River to Lake Erie—opened, 1825*
27 Sunday   *Daylight Savings ends; set clocks back*

October

Diary

Halloween

Temperature at witching hour: _____

The Best Costumes

A Poem on Boo!

The Tastiest Treats

The Worst Tricks

What We Gave as Treats

Design for a
Perfect Witch's Broom

A Memento of the Day

October

Sun	Mon	Tue	Wed	Thu	Fri	Sat
		1	2	3	4	5
6	7	8	9	10	11	12
13	14	15	16	17	18	19
20	21	22	23	24	25	26
27	28	29	30	31		

Dull November brings the blast;
Then the leaves are whirling fast.

Sarah Coleridge

"Liberty, like day, breaks on the soul, and by
a flash from Heaven fires all the faculties
with glorious joy."

William Cowper

To one who has been long in the city pent,
'Tis very sweet to look into the fair
And open face of heaven.

John Keats

Appointments
28 Monday
151' statue, "Liberty Enlightening the World," inaugurated in NY, 1886
29 Tuesday
Poet John Keats born, 1795
30 Wednesday
Baseball player Ted Williams born, 1918
31 Thursday
Halloween. Good night, sleep tight, don't let the vampires bite!
1 Friday
All Saints Day *Sculptor Benvenuto Cellini born, 1500*
2 Saturday
All Souls Day *2 Presidents—Polk & Harding—born, 1795 & 1865*
3 Sunday
Guidebook-publisher Karl Baedeker born, 1801

October November

November

Sun	Mon	Tue	Wed	Thu	Fri	Sat
					1	2
3	4	5	6	7	8	9
10	11	12	13	14	15	16
17	18	19	20	21	22	23
24	25	26	27	28	29	30

I love vast libraries; yet there is doubt
If one be better with them or without,—
Unless he use them wisely, and, indeed,
Knows the high art of what and how to read.

J.G. Saxe, "The Library"

"I never met a man I didn't like."
Will Rogers

Appointments
4 Monday   *Humorist Will Rogers born, 1879*
5 Tuesday   *Historian Will Durant born, 1885*
6 Wednesday   *Actress Lily Langtry made American debut, in NYC, 1882*
7 Thursday   *Museum of Modern Art, in NYC, opened, 1929*
8 Friday   *Astronomer Edmund Halley—of Halley's Comet fame—born, 1656*
9 Saturday   *Writer Ivan Turgenev born, 1818*
10 Sunday   *Actor Richard Burton born, 1925*

November

Diary

November

Sun	Mon	Tue	Wed	Thu	Fri	Sat
					1	2
3	4	5	6	7	8	9
10	11	12	13	14	15	16
17	18	19	20	21	22	23
24	25	26	27	28	29	30

Oh, the Roman was a rogue,
  He erat was, you bettum;
He ran his automobilus
  And smoked his cigarettum.
He wore a diamond studibus
  And elegant cravattum,
A maxima cum laude shirt,
  And such a stylish hattum.

Thomas R. Ybarra, "Lay of Ancient Rome"

Appointments
11 Monday *Remembrance Day—World War I ended, 1918*
12 Tuesday *Sculptor Auguste Rodin born, 1840*
13 Wednesday *A brilliant shower of stars seen worldwide, 1831, 1832, 1833*
14 Thursday *1st streetcar in the world—horsedrawn—began business, NYC, 1832*
15 Friday *White corpuscles discovered in blood, by Dr. A. Carrel, 1923*
16 Saturday *Composer Paul Hindemith born, 1895*
17 Sunday *Actor Rock Hudson born, 1925*

November

Diary

Birds of a Feather

"...There was a goose [in Ireland], which, by some accident, was left solitary, without mate or offspring, gander or gosling.

"Now, it happened...that the miller's wife had set a number of duck eggs under a hen...and the ducklings, as soon as they came forth, ran with natural instinct to the water, and the hen was in a sad pucker—her maternity urging her to follow the brood, and her selfishness disposing her to keep on dry land. In the meanwhile, up sailed the goose, and with a noisy gabble, which certainly meant, leave them to my care, she swam up and down with the ducklings; and when they were tired with their aquatic excursion, she consigned them to the hen's care. The next morning, down came again the ducklings to the pond, and there was the goose waiting, and there stood the hen in her great flustration. On this occasion [and until the ducklings grew up]...the hen jumped on the goose's back, and there sat, the ducklings swimming, and the goose and the hen after them, up and down the pond."

Rev. C. Ottway, "American Agriculturist," September 1848

November

Sun	Mon	Tue	Wed	Thu	Fri	Sat
					1	2
3	4	5	6	7	8	9
10	11	12	13	14	15	16
17	18	19	20	21	22	23
24	25	26	27	28	29	30

Appointments

18 Monday

Pollster George Gallup born, 1901

19 Tuesday

Lincoln gave his Gettysburg Address, 1863

20 Wednesday

Signer of Declaration of Independence, Oliver Wolcott, born, 1726

21 Thursday

Great American Smokeout. Your year to try?
Oxfam Fast Day—begun 1974

22 Friday

Composer Benjamin Britten born, 1913

23 Saturday

Comedian/musician Harpo Marx born, 1893

24 Sunday

Rag musician/composer Scott Joplin born, 1868

November

Diary

Today's weather:

Thanksgiving Day

(See October 14 and November 28)

What This Day Has Meant

A Memento of the Day

Menu *or* Special Recipe

A Prayer of Thanksgiving

November

Sun	Mon	Tue	Wed	Thu	Fri	Sat
					1	2
3	4	5	6	7	8	9
10	11	12	13	14	15	16
17	18	19	20	21	22	23
24	25	26	27	28	29	30

Chill December brings the sleet,
Blazing fire and Christmas treat.
Sarah Coleridge

Neigh, It's a Mechanical Substitute

"Some time ago, a gentleman...was possessed with the singular notion that [he could]...construct a machine to evolve the same action as a galloping horse.... The 'rider' sets himself upon an ordinary leather saddle, his feet being in fixed stirrups, and his hands grasping a handle.... Beneath the platform are four padded buffers—corresponding to the horse's feet—and by the weight and motion of the operator's body, these buffers strike or bump...so that with a little practice an automatic imitation of horse-exercise can be produced... For those condemned to sedentary employment, its daily use is said to be attended with beneficial results."
"Chamber's Journal, November 28, 1885

Appointments

25 Monday

Philanthropist Andrew Carnegie born, 1835

26 Tuesday

Thanksgiving Day 1st celebrated nationally, 1789

27 Wednesday

The Hoosac Tunnel in northwestern Massachusetts completed, 1873

28 Thursday

Thanksgiving Day

29 Friday

Writer Louisa May Alcott born, 1832

30 Saturday

Writer/humorist Samuel Clemens (Mark Twain) born, 1835

1 Sunday

Advent
Mystery writer Rex Stout born, 1886

November December

Diary

December

Sun	Mon	Tue	Wed	Thu	Fri	Sat
1	2	3	4	5	6	7
8	9	10	11	12	13	14
15	16	17	18	19	20	21
22	23	24	25	26	27	28
29	30	31				

"...Slaves that once conceive the glowing thought of freedom, in the hope itself possess all that the contest calls for; spirit, strength, the scorn of danger, and united hearts, the surest presage of the good they seek."

William Cowper

"But when he speaks, what elocution flows! Soft as the fleeces of descending snows The copious accents fall, with easy art; Melting they fall, and sink into the heart."

Alexander Pope

Appointments
2 Monday   Opera star Maria Callas born, 1923
3 Tuesday   Novelist Joseph Conrad born, 1857
4 Wednesday   American Antislavery Society formed, 1833
5 Thursday   Cartoonist Walt Disney born, 1901
6 Friday   St. Nicholas Day
7 Saturday   Waxwork Museum creator Marie Tussaud born, 1761
8 Sunday   Hanukah begins: Festival of Lights Humorist/cartoonist James Thurber born, 1894

December

Diary

December

Sun	Mon	Tue	Wed	Thu	Fri	Sat
1	2	3	4	5	6	7
8	9	10	11	12	13	14
15	16	17	18	19	20	21
22	23	24	25	26	27	28
29	30	31				

Appointments

'Hope is the thing with feathers'
Hope is the thing with feathers
That perches in the soul,
And sings the tune without the words,
And never stops at all.

And sweetest in the gale is heard;
And sore must be the storm
That could abash the little bird
That kept so many warm.

I've heard it in the chillest land,
And on the strangest sea;
Yet, never, in extremity,
It asked a crumb of me.
Emily Dickinson

9 Monday

Poet John Milton born, 1608

10 Tuesday

Poet Emily Dickinson born, 1830

11 Wednesday

Composer Hector Berlioz born, 1803

12 Thursday

Actor Edward G. Robinson born, 1893

13 Friday

1st US savings bank chartered, 1817

14 Saturday

Prophet Michael de Nostradamus born, 1503

15 Sunday

Mistletoe Day
1st Professor of Law, James Wilson, appointed, U. of PA, 1791

December

Diary

December

Sun	Mon	Tue	Wed	Thu	Fri	Sat
1	2	3	4	5	6	7
8	9	10	11	12	13	14
15	16	17	18	19	20	21
22	23	24	25	26	27	28
29	30	31				

O Winter! ruler of the inverted year,
Thy scatter'd hair with
      sleet-like ashes fill'd,
Thy breath congeal'd upon thy lips,
      thy cheeks
Fring'd with a beard made white
      with other snows
Than those of age; thy forehead
      wrapt in clouds,
A leafless branch thy sceptre,
      and thy throne
A sliding car indebted to no wheels,
But urged by storms along
      its slippery way;
I love thee, all unlovely as thou seem'st,
And dreaded as thou art.

William Cowper

Appointments

16 Monday

Anthropologist Margaret Mead born, 1901

17 Tuesday

Orville & Wilbur Wright flew at Kittyhawk NC, 1903 (Orville first)

18 Wednesday

Slavery abolished with ratification of Amendment XIII, 1865

19 Thursday

Benjamin Franklin 1st published Poor Richard's Almanac, 1732

20 Friday

Rubber magnate Harvey Samuel Firestone born, 1868

21 Saturday

Winter Solstice: Winter begins
Pilgrims landed at Plymouth Rock, 1620

22 Sunday

Composer Giacomo Puccini born, 1858

December

Diary

Christmas

Today's weather:

A Christmas Blessing

A Story of Christmas Eve

Menu or Special Recipe

Those Who Shared This Day

Some
Memorable
Presents

A Memento of the Day

December						
Sun	Mon	Tue	Wed	Thu	Fri	Sat
1	2	3	4	5	6	7
8	9	10	11	12	13	14
15	16	17	18	19	20	21
22	23	24	25	26	27	28
29	30	31				

The night is calm and cloudless,
And still as still can be,
And the stars come forth to listen
To the music of the sea.
They gather, and gather, and gather,
Until they crowd the sky,
And listen in breathless silence,
To the solemn litany.

Henry Wadsworth Longfellow, "Christus. Golden Legend"

"Of all human inventions, the most
worthless is an excuse."
Saying on an 1880's trade card

Appointments

23 Monday

Dancer José Greco born, 1918

24 Tuesday

Frontiersman Kit Carson born, 1809

25 Wednesday

Christmas

26 Thursday

Boxing Day & St. Stephen's Day

27 Friday

Astronomer Johann Kepler born, 1571

28 Saturday

Brewer John Molson born, 1763

29 Sunday

Raincoat originator William Macintosh born, 1776

December

Diary

This world is not so bad a world
  As some would like to make it;
Though whether good, or whether bad,
  Depends on how we take it.
Michael Wentworth Beck

Once again it's Janus' time
To reign o'er deep winter's clime.
Grace McFarland

1986
January

Sun	Mon	Tue	Wed	Thu	Fri	Sat
			1	2	3	4
5	6	7	8	9	10	11
12	13	14	15	16	17	18
19	20	21	22	23	24	25
26	27	28	29	30	31	

Appointments

30 Monday

Philanthropist Simon Guggenheim born, 1867

31 Tuesday

Clean Air Act signed into law, 1970

1 Wednesday

New Year's Day, 1986

2 Thursday

Patriot Paul Revere born, 1735

3 Friday

March of Dimes organized, 1938

4 Saturday

Fairy tale author Jacob Grimm born, 1785

5 Sunday

1st woman US governor, Wyoming's Nellie Taylor Ross, in office 1925

December January

Diary

To Wish you a Happy Birthday

Birthdays

Birthdays come but once a year,
  Leap birthdays once in four.
May all the birthdays listed here
  Be followed by many more!

Weddings & Anniversaries

Love makes the world go 'round;
  That's what the poets and songsters say.
After many turns, here will be found
  Records of '85 loving days!

Graduations, Promotions & Milestone Days

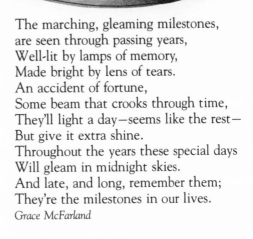

The marching, gleaming milestones,
are seen through passing years,
Well-lit by lamps of memory,
Made bright by lens of tears.
An accident of fortune,
Some beam that crooks through time,
They'll light a day—seems like the rest—
But give it extra shine.
Throughout the years these special days
Will gleam in midnight skies.
And late, and long, remember them;
They're the milestones in our lives.
Grace McFarland

The Language of Flowers

Sentiments can be expressed through the exchange of flowers. In a 19th century book on etiquette, the following unconcluded "conversation" was given.

The gentleman presents a red rose —"I love you." The lady admits a partial reciprocation of the sentiment by returning a purple pansy — "You occupy my thoughts." The gentleman presses his suit still further by an everlasting pea —"Wilt thou go with me?" The lady replies by a daisy, in which she says —"I will think of it."

Below are but a few of the scores of flowers, herbs and evergreens given meaning.

Acacia *Friendship*

Amaryllis *Beautiful but timid*

Anemone *Forsaken*

Apple Blossom *Preference*

Arbutus *Thee only do I love*

Aster *Variety*

Bachelors' Button *Hope*

Buttercup *Riches*

Camellia *Gratitude*

Carnation *Pure and deep love*

Chrysanthemum *A desolate heart*

Four-Leaved Clover *Be mine*

Red Clover *Industry*

Columbine *Anxious and trembling*

Cowslip *Native grace*

Dahlia *Dignity and elegance*

Daffodil *Unrequited love*

Daisy *I will think about it*

Dandelion *Coquetry*

Forget-me-not *Do not forget*

Fuchsia *Taste or frugality*

Geranium *I prefer you*

Gladiolus *Ready armed*

Hawthorn *Hope*

Hibiscus *Delicate beauty*

Holly *Am I forgotten?*

Hyacinth *Constancy*

Hydrangea *Heartlessness*

Iris *A message for thee*

Jonquil *Desire*

Larkspur *Lightness or fickleness*

Purple Lilac *First emotions of love*

White Lilac *Youth*

Lily of the Valley *Return of happiness*

Magnolia *Love of nature*

Marigold *Sacred affection*

Morning Glory *Affection*

Nasturtium *Patriotism*

Pennyroyal *Flee away*

Phlox *Our hearts are united*

Poppy *Consolation*

Primrose *Modest worth or silent love*

Rhododendrom *Agitation*

Red Rose *I love you*

White Rose *Silence*

Wild Rose *Simplicity*

Yellow Rose *Unfaithfulness*

Rue *Disdain*

Snapdragon *Presumption*

Sunflower *Lofty and wise thoughts*

Sweet Pea *A meeting*

Sweet William *Gallantry*

Thorn Apple *Disguise*

Violet *Faithfulness*

Wall Flower *Fidelity in misfortune*

Water Lily *Eloquence*

Zinnia *I mourn your absence*

Birthstones & Flowers

January
Garnet
Carnation or Snowdrop

February
Amethyst
Primrose or Violet

March
Aquamarine or Bloodstone
Jonquil or Daffodil

April
Diamond
Daisy or Sweet Pea

May
Emerald
Hawthorn or Lily of the Valley

June
Moonstone, Alexandrite or Pearl
Rose or Honeysuckle

July
Ruby
Water Lily, Larkspur or Delphinium

August
Peridot or Sardonyx
Gladiolus or Poppy

September
Sapphire
Morning Glory or Aster

October
Opal or Tourmaline
Calendula or Marigold

November
Topaz
Chrysanthemum

December
Turquoise or Zircon
Holly, Narcissus or Poinsettia

Gifts for Wedding Anniversaries

It has long been the custom to give anniversary gifts. As it is expected that gold be given to the celebrating couple on their 50th—Golden—Anniversary, so it has evolved that all the anniversaries up to the fifteenth have special gifts, and every fifth one beyond that also has an appropriate gift. Those couples who celebrate beyond their 75th Anniversary surely have the most precious gift of all—their lasting love for each other.

1st	Paper or plastic		14th	Ivory or agate
2nd	Cotton		15th	Crystal
3rd	Leather		20th	Porcelain or china
4th	Silk or linen		25th	Silver
5th	Wood		30th	Pearl
6th	Iron		35th	Coral or jade
7th	Wool, copper or brass		40th	Ruby or garnet
8th	Electric appliances or bronze		45th	Sapphire or tourmaline
9th	Pottery		50th	Gold
10th	Tin or aluminum		55th	Emerald or turquoise
11th	Steel		60th	Diamond
12th	Linen or silk		75th	Diamond
13th	Lace			

Musings on the Year

1985

January
Sun	Mon	Tue	Wed	Thu	Fri	Sat
		1	2	3	4	5
6	7	8	9	10	11	12
13	14	15	16	17	18	19
20	21	22	23	24	25	26
27	28	29	30	31		

February
Sun	Mon	Tue	Wed	Thu	Fri	Sat
					1	2
3	4	5	6	7	8	9
10	11	12	13	14	15	16
17	18	19	20	21	22	23
24	25	26	27	28		

March
Sun	Mon	Tue	Wed	Thu	Fri	Sat
					1	2
3	4	5	6	7	8	9
10	11	12	13	14	15	16
17	18	19	20	21	22	23
24	25	26	27	28	29	30
31						

April
Sun	Mon	Tue	Wed	Thu	Fri	Sat
	1	2	3	4	5	6
7	8	9	10	11	12	13
14	15	16	17	18	19	20
21	22	23	24	25	26	27
28	29	30				

May
Sun	Mon	Tue	Wed	Thu	Fri	Sat
			1	2	3	4
5	6	7	8	9	10	11
12	13	14	15	16	17	18
19	20	21	22	23	24	25
26	27	28	29	30	31	

June
Sun	Mon	Tue	Wed	Thu	Fri	Sat
						1
2	3	4	5	6	7	8
9	10	11	12	13	14	15
16	17	18	19	20	21	22
23	24	25	26	27	28	29
30						

July
Sun	Mon	Tue	Wed	Thu	Fri	Sat
	1	2	3	4	5	6
7	8	9	10	11	12	13
14	15	16	17	18	19	20
21	22	23	24	25	26	27
28	29	30	31			

August
Sun	Mon	Tue	Wed	Thu	Fri	Sat
				1	2	3
4	5	6	7	8	9	10
11	12	13	14	15	16	17
18	19	20	21	22	23	24
25	26	27	28	29	30	31

September
Sun	Mon	Tue	Wed	Thu	Fri	Sat
1	2	3	4	5	6	7
8	9	10	11	12	13	14
15	16	17	18	19	20	21
22	23	24	25	26	27	28
29	30					

October
Sun	Mon	Tue	Wed	Thu	Fri	Sat
		1	2	3	4	5
6	7	8	9	10	11	12
13	14	15	16	17	18	19
20	21	22	23	24	25	26
27	28	29	30	31		

November
Sun	Mon	Tue	Wed	Thu	Fri	Sat
					1	2
3	4	5	6	7	8	9
10	11	12	13	14	15	16
17	18	19	20	21	22	23
24	25	26	27	28	29	30

December
Sun	Mon	Tue	Wed	Thu	Fri	Sat
1	2	3	4	5	6	7
8	9	10	11	12	13	14
15	16	17	18	19	20	21
22	23	24	25	26	27	28
29	30	31				

1986

January
Sun	Mon	Tue	Wed	Thu	Fri	Sat
			1	2	3	4
5	6	7	8	9	10	11
12	13	14	15	16	17	18
19	20	21	22	23	24	25
26	27	28	29	30	31	

February
Sun	Mon	Tue	Wed	Thu	Fri	Sat
						1
2	3	4	5	6	7	8
9	10	11	12	13	14	15
16	17	18	19	20	21	22
23	24	25	26	27	28	

March
Sun	Mon	Tue	Wed	Thu	Fri	Sat
						1
2	3	4	5	6	7	8
9	10	11	12	13	14	15
16	17	18	19	20	21	22
23	24	25	26	27	28	29
30	31					

April
Sun	Mon	Tue	Wed	Thu	Fri	Sat
		1	2	3	4	5
6	7	8	9	10	11	12
13	14	15	16	17	18	19
20	21	22	23	24	25	26
27	28	29	30			

May
Sun	Mon	Tue	Wed	Thu	Fri	Sat
				1	2	3
4	5	6	7	8	9	10
11	12	13	14	15	16	17
18	19	20	21	22	23	24
25	26	27	28	29	30	31

June
Sun	Mon	Tue	Wed	Thu	Fri	Sat
1	2	3	4	5	6	7
8	9	10	11	12	13	14
15	16	17	18	19	20	21
22	23	24	25	26	27	28
29	30					

July
Sun	Mon	Tue	Wed	Thu	Fri	Sat
		1	2	3	4	5
6	7	8	9	10	11	12
13	14	15	16	17	18	19
20	21	22	23	24	25	26
27	28	29	30	31		

August
Sun	Mon	Tue	Wed	Thu	Fri	Sat
					1	2
3	4	5	6	7	8	9
10	11	12	13	14	15	16
17	18	19	20	21	22	23
24	25	26	27	28	29	30
31						

September
Sun	Mon	Tue	Wed	Thu	Fri	Sat
	1	2	3	4	5	6
7	8	9	10	11	12	13
14	15	16	17	18	19	20
21	22	23	24	25	26	27
28	29	30				

October
Sun	Mon	Tue	Wed	Thu	Fri	Sat
			1	2	3	4
5	6	7	8	9	10	11
12	13	14	15	16	17	18
19	20	21	22	23	24	25
26	27	28	29	30	31	

November
Sun	Mon	Tue	Wed	Thu	Fri	Sat
						1
2	3	4	5	6	7	8
9	10	11	12	13	14	15
16	17	18	19	20	21	22
23	24	25	26	27	28	29
30						

December
Sun	Mon	Tue	Wed	Thu	Fri	Sat
	1	2	3	4	5	6
7	8	9	10	11	12	13
14	15	16	17	18	19	20
21	22	23	24	25	26	27
28	29	30	31			

Our Family Index

A ❖ B	I ❖ J	Q ❖ R
C ❖ D	K ❖ L	S ❖ T
E ❖ F	M ❖ N	U ❖ V ❖ W
G ❖ H	O ❖ P	X ❖ Y ❖ Z